You Can't Be Serious!

Stu Campbell

Enjoy!

Stu Campbell

ISBN 978-0-9675164-4-8

Cover and text design by D.K. Luraas

Printed and bound in the United States of America

Contents

Word Games 1

Suitable 3

Two Bad Habits 8

Divorce 10

A New Hawker 12

Retirement? 15

Women's Lib 17

Surprise! 20

Becoming a Bum 25

Near Death 29

Making Amends 32

Forgetfulness? 35

A Profession? 37

Returning Borrowed Goods 40

Do People Know What They're Doing? 45

Perception 49

A Free Pass! 52

Out of My Class 54

Working Too Hard 58
Hunt and Peck 60
Coincidence 63
Travel Tips 65
Candy? 68
Just Do It 72
No Rest for the Wicked, or Even the Weary 81
Perplexed 85
Proper Demonstrations 87
A Positive Error 90
Book Signings 95
Trouble Again 98

Word Games

I'm always amused at some of our seemingly innocent mannerisms. For example, when I walk into a restaurant to get something to eat, and see the sign,

PLEASE WAIT TO BE SEATED

and no one is available to seat me—I figure all the help is sitting in the back room playing cards. When I'm finally noticed, the hostess generally asks as she approaches, "Just one?"

Of course, just one, I think. *How many of me do you see?*

I've heard this so much, I've got plumb tired of listening to it, so I decided to do something about it. The next time I was asked, "Just one?" I decided to reply with something different. What, you ask?

I decided that the next time I was asked the obviously stupid question, I would reply with the answer, "Unless you're goin' to join me!"

That reply has brought some interesting responses, from "Oh, I'd love to, but I have to work," to "I can't tonight, 'cause I'm working," or "I would, but I'm working."

I often wonder if they *would* join me if they weren't working.

That response has worked well, bringing many a smile to some haggard hostesses. It's worked so well that I started using it at all the restaurants and was almost disappointed when I didn't see the sign. I got to using it so much, it almost became a habit.

It became so much of a habit that I almost abused it.

I was checking into a motel one night when I heard the ever-mentioned question, "Just one?"

I was totally caught off guard because I was admiring the gal behind the counter. She was really good-looking with big expressive brown eyes and long blonde hair. She was very beautiful, and my mind got to wandering.

When I heard, "Just one?" I almost blurted out, "Unless you're goin' to join me!" But I managed to restrain myself and got a room, alone, without further incident.

Suitable

Driving around the country selling books can be a little tiresome, a little boring, a little discouraging, and a lot lonely. It's a good chance to see the country and take in the various sights, read the various roadside historical markers, and generally make a living without having a regular forty-plus hour a week job.

I get real disgusted in the Pacific Time Zone. I live in the Mountain Time Zone, and am in the habit of waking up around 4:30 or a quarter to five in the morning, no matter what time zone I'm in. In the Pacific Time Zone, I have an extra hour to kill before I can start hitting the bookstores, saddle shops, and museums where I might sell some books. At home, in the Mountain Time Zone, the stores usually open around ten, so I've got around five hours with nothing to do.

In the Central Time Zone, it's a little easier, there's an hour less time to waste before I can start selling.

That makes it a little more convenient, but the day still ends an hour earlier. It's an adjustment I have to make.

In Pocatello, Idaho, I was on a book selling trip, and having a pretty good time. Book sales were good, the weather was good, and I was enjoying myself on the road. But, I was a little discouraged as I hadn't learned how to tell what kind of a store the bookstore was by the name of the bookstore, and consequently I was making a lot of stops at specialty bookstores such as New Age or Metaphysical bookstores and religious or bible bookstores, places that generally don't have an interest in cowboy stories.

I was walking along the sidewalk, not paying much attention to where I was going, thinking about how I could improve my sales pitch. There were three book-shops located in this block, and it appeared they were all located within four or five doors of each other. As I walked along, deeply engaged in thought, I glanced into the window of the store I was passing. Books! I had located one of my objectives.

Without thinking I entered the store, and instantly I was in a different world! I was surrounded by walls about eight feet high, with a staircase leading to an upper floor, or mezzanine, on one side. Off to the side of the stairs was a big guy sitting behind a cash register where he could look down on all who entered.

A glance around the walls behind the big guy told me I had entered a pornographic bookstore!

I really didn't know what to do. I sure didn't think any of the stuff I wrote had a place in a store such as this. I shuffled around some, feeling kind of lost, thinking I had made another poor choice. I mumbled, "I think I got the wrong store."

"What are you selling?" a gruff but friendly voice asked. He had noticed the books in my hands.

"I'm just traveling around peddlin' some books I wrote," I replied.

"Let's take a look at them," the big guy replied.

"They ain't much," I said. "Just some personal experience stuff I wrote. They're kinda fun books, kinda humorous."

"How much are they?"

I told him the retail price. I have a wholesale pricing structure so I can sell to bookstores and they can make some money. I really didn't think I would make a sale here.

"I'll buy them," said the big guy, reaching for his wallet. "I don't read this trash," he said, indicating the wall behind him.

I made the sale, and as I walked back to the truck to get more copies of the books to show to the other bookstores, I had the thought cross my mind, *I must be pretty good! I just sold my books to a porno bookstore!*

The more I traveled, the more I could work on my sales pitch. I couldn't really use a canned sales pitch, it just didn't seem natural to me. But I did need to have some ready answers to commonly asked questions.

The two most frequently asked questions are, "What are they about?" and "Are they children's books?"

To the first question, the standard answer became, "They're short stories about ranch life, rodeo, the dude business, cowboys and horses in general. They're kinda humorous, just fun books."

The standard answer to the second question became, "They're not really kid's books, but they are suitable for all members of the family. As an author, I can only write about those things I know about, so consequently there ain't no sex or violence in them."

This approach worked so well that I started using it all the time. It would generally bring a laugh and put my prospective customers at ease. This worked particularly well with the lady bookstore owners or managers.

"That's good!" Their reply would quite often be most emphatic.

I remember one instance with a particularly good-looking lady store manager; I made my standard reply,

"As an author, I can only write about those things I know about, so consequently there ain't no sex or violence in them."

"What a shame!" she exclaimed, as she laughed. "What a shame!"

We could fix that right now, I almost blurted out. But I kept my mouth shut.

I wasn't surprised when I completed the sale.

Two Bad Habits

I really don't like to offend people, particularly when they're trying to be nice to me. However, most of the time people just simply don't understand.

For example, people seem to take offense when I refuse a beer or a cocktail or a glass of wine. I don't understand why they take offense—if I don't drink it, that just leaves more for them.

I get kind of frustrated constantly refusing an alcoholic drink and then having to explain why. So I started to make up ridiculous reasons why I didn't care to drink with those that proffered me a drink. After a time this became real absurd, so I decided to tell the truth.

When folks offer me a drink now, if I have time, I simply explain to them, "I used to drink, and I drank a lot, and for a skinny old cowboy, I held it quite well. But every now and then I'd get drunk. An every time

I'd get drunk, I'd get married! Then, I'd have to stay drunk to stay married! I just couldn't afford two bad habits!"

That answer seemed to satisfy most folks and it took a lot of pressure off me.

Divorce

Divorce is always a messy subject. But when a feller has been through it more than once, people look at him kinda strange. When he's been through it more than twice, people begin to think there's something wrong with him. When he's been through it four times, like I have, people not only look at you strange, they know something is wrong and they begin to expect some sort of explanation.

Such was the case with me, and I had to tell them something. So, when the subject came up and I was asked to voice an opinion, I didn't want to sound like a whining ex-husband, and I didn't want to go into much detail, consequently I would tell the folks this.

"The first time I was divorced, that wife got all my money. I didn't have much at the time, but she got it all!

"The second time I was divorced, that wife got all my cows. I used to have a little cow ranch over in Utah, an' she got all my cows! That was tough 'cause I had some really good cows!

"The third time I was divorced, that wife got the ranch!

"The last time I was divorced, you know I kinda feel sorry for that gal. After the first three, there wasn't much to give over to her. I saw her about ten or twelve years ago in Granby, Colorado, an' she asked me, 'How you doing?'

"I'd always felt a little guilty about not giving her anything in that divorce, but I didn't want to tell her I was doin' good for fear I might have to give her something, an' I didn't want to lie to her an' tell her I was doin' bad, so I just looked her right straight dead in the eyes an' says, 'Since you've been gone, I've been so miserable, it's like you never left!'"

A New Hawker

Every now and then, I'm asked to do a book signing at one of the retail outlets that handle my books. Most of the time these are fun deals and we sell a few books.

I'm careful to tell the retail managers that if I were famous, more people would show up. But I'm just an old cowboy, not a movie star or a person that has done something that would bring world-wide acclaim.

I had a book signing in Loveland, Colorado, on a Sunday in December of 2009. The day before, I had done a book signing at their sister store, JAX, in Fort Collins. The signing had gone well; we sold twenty some odd books.

I was looking forward to the signing in Loveland. My youngest daughter, Lorrie, lives in Loveland with my then eight-year-old granddaughter, Jade. I had invited them to come to the signing and was looking forward to seeing them.

The store management had set us up with a table and chair, along with fudge and coffee towards the rear of the store by the hardware section. I would have liked it better if we had been set up closer to the front of the store, or closer to the saddle and tack department, but I had to make do with what we had.

Lorrie and Jade showed up and we had a real good visit, but we weren't talking to a lot of people because there weren't a lot of people walking around in the hardware section.

Jade was becoming a little bored, or perhaps a little frustrated with my constant teasing. I decided to put her to work.

"Sit here," I said. "I think these people would rather look at a good lookin' little girl like you rather than an ugly old cowboy like me."

It took some convincing, but I finally got Jade to sit at the table. She was a little uncomfortable.

"Tell each one of these folks to buy a book," I told her.

She made some feeble attempts to entice people into looking at the books on display. She didn't have much success.

"Tell these people that if they buy a book they can have some free fudge an' coffee," I said. "Hold up a book when you say that, and these people will stop and look at them and we might make a sale!"

It took her a time or two trying this out, but she got warmed up to it and a few people did stop. When she was asked what the books were about, she didn't know what to say.

"You have to ask my Grandpa," she would answer. "He wrote them."

I would answer the questions.

Jade did a pretty good job hawking books for me that day. She became perplexed when someone volunteered to pay her on the spot.

"Take the money! Take the money!" I hollered.

That was good for a laugh, as I signed the books and told the customers they could pay for them at the register.

We sold a few books and had a good time. I had Jade hawking for me because I figured the day would be a bust anyway, just because of where they had located us in the store. It was a good day anyway.

Retirement?

Penny has always been a good friend. We enjoyed dancing together, and generally just tossing the bull back and forth. We never did get real close, contemplating marriage or anything like that, we were just real good friends. I used to see Penny about once or twice a year, and we always had fun.

I wasn't surprised much when I heard Penny and Bud were going to get married. We all knew each other; we had a lot in common. After they were married, Bud used to tease me about him being the lucky one because he married Penny. I took the ribbing good-naturedly, but secretly envied him.

I guess Bud had been married to Penny about a year when he retired. I met up with them a few months after Bud's retirement.

"How are you gettin' along in your retirement?" I asked. I knew Bud was looking forward to taking it easy.

"It's been pretty rough," said Bud.

"Rough? How can retirement be rough? Are you bored with nothing to do?"

"No. I've got plenty to do. The day after I retired, I was looking forward to relaxing—watching television, and generally taking it easy. But then Penny said, 'Now that you're retired you can remodel the kitchen, paint the outside of the house, and catch up on all those things you told me you didn't have time for.' I've got more to do now than when I was working! I don't even get a day off! Penny is driving me pretty hard."

"Do you have to do the cooking, too?" I asked.

"Sometimes," answered Bud. "But sometimes I get so caught up in a project, I can't find the time to cook."

"I'm sure glad you got her, Bud!"

I wasn't quite so envious anymore!

Women's Lib

I'm not so sure that women's lib is a good idea—for the gals that is. I would think that the women would have appreciated having doors opened for them, having men take off their hats when introduced, and just being nicely treated in general.

I've had a hard time adjusting to the change. Coming from the "old school" so to speak, I've always felt a little uncomfortable when a woman held a door open for me. I would always try to hold the door for her, but some of the gals were quite adamant about holding the door for me.

"You come on in first," I would say.

"No. That's all right, you come!"

In order to prevent an argument, I'd usually just go on, making sure I thanked the gal properly. But sometimes that mere "thank you" didn't seem like enough.

What else could I say to let a woman know that her act was very kind? I didn't lose much sleep over it, but it was still kinda embarrassing to me to have a woman hold the door for me.

Again, one day a woman held the door for me. Without thinking, I entered the building and as graciously as I could, I thanked the gal. Then, without thinking I added, "You know, where I come from, the men hold the door for the women!"

The gal smiled a little.

"But I just want you to know that someone did take the time to train you right!"

On another occasion, a friend's wife asked me, when I held the door open for her and some other ladies, "How can I get John to open the door for me? He used to be so attentive and do little things like that all the time, but lately he's become a little lax."

I've never been considered a marriage counselor, so jokingly I said, "Next time John takes you to a movie, take along a flashlight and a magazine."

"A flashlight and a magazine? What for?" she asked.

"When John gets out of the car and starts toward the theater without you, just stay in the car. You can read the magazine by the light of the flashlight while you're waiting for him to notice that you're not there. It will give you something to do while you're waiting."

I saw her a few months later … she told me that my idea worked!

Surprise!

Some years ago, when three of my grandkids were only about six or seven years old, I used to take a surprise to them every time I'd go to Salt Lake City to visit them. One year, I decided to take over some Colorado Lottery scratch tickets.

The scratch tickets I took were the crossword kind, where a person scratches off the letters on the puzzle to form words. The more words that are formed, the more money a person can win. Its kind of a fun game; it only takes about ten minutes and a person can win up to twenty or thirty thousand dollars.

With the idea that these kids could win vast sums of money, and at their tender ages might spend it unwisely, before I gave them their scratch tickets, I told them that they would have to split any of their winnings with me, fifty-fifty. The rest they would split equally among themselves. If they had a big winner, I would redeem their tickets back in Colorado and deposit their winnings in each one of their savings accounts that I had set up at a Credit Union.

They readily agreed, and eagerly started to find words from their letters on the tickets. When they were done, I scrutinized the tickets to determine what their winnings were. As it turned out, two of the girls hadn't won anything, but one of the girls had won nine dollars.

"Okay," I said, as we sat down to figure the payout. "Now it's time to pay off the winners. All you girls agreed that we were goin' to split the winnings fifty-fifty, correct?"

The girls readily agreed, knowing that they would have some money to spend, probably on candy at the grocery store. But I decided to have some fun with them.

"It looks like you've won nine dollars. Half of nine dollars is $4.50. So, at this point I owe you $4.50, an' I get $4.50, right?"

The girls seemed pleased with this prospect.

"But," I continued, "the tickets cost $15.00. Half of $15.00 is $7.50, so you owe me $7.50 less $4.50 which is three dollars, right?"

The girls looked a little dismayed, and I don't think they quite understood what was happening. They started to voice some objections, but I wouldn't let them interrupt.

"I had to fill up with gas in Granby and that came to $35.00; half of $35.00 is $17.50. So now you owe me $20.50!"

The girls were showing some frustration, and one of them said, "You brought us a surprise, but you're making us pay for it! That's not fair!"

"But I'm not done yet," I continued, "I had to get some supper and that came to about ten dollars. Half of ten is five, so now you owe me $25.50. Then I had to get a motel room, an' that came to $36.00 an' some change, but we'll just call it $36.00. Half of $36.00 is $18.00. Then I had to get more gas, an' that came to $25.00, an' half of that is $12.50."

I had a piece of paper and was trying to keep track of the totals. I had a total of $56.00.

All three of the girls were becoming quite frustrated and were telling me that this wasn't right. And they were telling me quite loudly.

I pretended to ignore them and their protestations and continued, "Then I had to get some breakfast. That came to six bucks. Half of six is three. Is that right?"

I couldn't get the girls to agree that half of six is three. They were really concerned that they were losing their original $4.50.

"Then, I had to buy a new shirt so I would look good for you girls, and that came to about $22.00. Half of that is $11.00. Now the way I have this figured is that you girls owe me about $70.00. Is that right?I held up the paper for their examination. They ignored it. They were becoming quite vocal in their protest.

"If it's going to cost us seventy dollars for you to come and visit us, we don't want you to come and visit anymore!"

"But," I replied, "I only brought you this surprise because I want to see you happy and I love you!"

"If you love us, how come you're trying to cheat us?"

I didn't have a response for that, and I really wasn't trying to cheat the girls. I was just having some fun.

As it turned out, I ended up giving Ashley the nine dollars she had won on her ticket and, feeling sorry for Samantha and Kourtney because they hadn't won anything, I gave each one of them five dollars.

One of the girls remarked, "You can come and visit us anytime you want, as long as we don't have to pay for it!"

"Do you want me to bring you some more scratch tickets?" I asked.

"NO!" The response was unanimous and adamant.

My daughter had been watching the proceedings with her girls, and she said, "You're having entirely too much fun with your grandkids, Grandpa!"

Becoming a Bum

For the last number of years, I've been a ski instructor. That's a little odd for an old cowboy, but I like to ski. I thought when I sold my rental horse stable and kind of semi-retired, I'd have a lot of spare time and I could do a lot of skiing in the winter. However, I can't afford to ski. I found out that when you're a ski instructor, you get a season pass for free. So, in the winter of 2000, I became a ski instructor.

January of 2010 started out alright, although due to economic conditions around the entire country, business was a little slow. I only teach skiing Monday through Friday because it gets real busy on the weekends, and I feel it's too crowded to do a good job of teaching. Consequently, I have the weekends off and can spend a lot of time watching football on television.

For the last four or five years, I've just rented a motel room on a monthly basis because it's cheaper than renting a house and putting down big monetary deposits for the house and utilities. The room has everything I need—a microwave, small fridge, T.V., and a bathroom. I've spent a lot of time in cow camps that had a lot less.

A big part of my daily routine is to get up in the morning, start the coffee, and shave. Shaving is a big thing for me, as I kinda feel like I'm undressed if I don't shave. But I really don't like to do it.

So when I woke up Saturday morning, January 9, 2010, I decided not to shave. I didn't have to go anywhere; I had everything I needed, and looked forward to spending the day inside, watching the wild card playoffs on T.V. I did just that, and then got interested in some movie and actually didn't get to bed until around eleven o'clock.

I generally wake up around 4:30 or a quarter of five, and I really thought it would be kinda nice to sleep in until six or maybe even seven. I'm a pretty sound sleeper and can sleep through just about anything.

I was really surprised when a guy busted down my door at about 5:30.

What the hell's going on? My first thought was that I was being robbed.

"The building's on fire! Get out of here!" The fireman that broke the door in wasn't too polite.

I quickly got dressed. I got my teeth, my saddle, my computer, and my golf clubs and threw them in the back of the truck. I also grabbed a handful of shirts.

The fireman did make the comment, "I think we can save this end of the building."

I got my truck out of the way and let the firemen do their job. I did feel kinda helpless just watching from a distance and not being able to do anything. I decided to drive around until I found a coffee shop and could get a cup. On Sunday morning at 5:30 in Granby, Colorado, there isn't much open.

Previously, I had made arrangements to take my seven-year-old granddaughter to breakfast in Grand Lake that Sunday morning. Seeing as I couldn't do anything at the motel, I headed to Grand Lake.

My granddaughter and her mom showed up at the restaurant, and much to my surprise, they already had heard about the fire. News, whether it's good or bad, travels fast in a small town.

After a longer than usual breakfast, I returned to the motel. The fire was out and the firemen were picking up their equipment. There were some Granby police officers keeping everyone off the premises and I was informed that I couldn't get into the building to retrieve my other belongings until they completed their investigation.

The management of the motel gave me another room in the west wing of the motel unaffected by the fire. I moved into that room, put away the stuff I had initially saved, and watched some of the playoff game.

The game turned out to be a blowout and I quickly lost interest in it. I went outside to visit with the cops and find out when I could get the rest of my stuff.

In visiting with the officials, I ran my hand over my chin. "I didn't get a shower this morning, and I haven't shaved for two days. I feel like a bum!" I said.

The cop that I was visiting with looked at me and said, "You haven't shaved, you're homeless—you are a bum!"

I guess it's alright to joke about a fairly serious thing when it's all over—when nobody's hurt and things turn out okay.

Near Death

I was at an author fair in Arizona in January. I didn't expect to sell much; I went down more to get out of the cold winter in Colorado. It was nice. The event was held outside and the sunshine was terrific. I couldn't believe the seventy-degree weather, and I was dreading the trip back. I could really get used to the temperature and considered making this an annual affair.

Visiting with the other authors was kinda nice. I even met some people that had lived in Grand Lake, which isn't too far from where I live. We traded quite a few stories about the area and some of the people we all knew. I even traded some of my books for other authors' works.

I don't get dressed up for these kinds of things—a clean pair of jeans, a clean shirt, and a relatively clean hat is about all I need. I do knock some of the horse manure off my boots. People that come to buy my books expect to see a cowboy, although those in the know can tell I'm a cowboy even when I've got a suit and tie on.

We were sitting out front of the store, just chewing the fat, when a car pulled up. The license plates were from Virginia. I let the other authors greet the folks, and just sat there watching. I don't try to sell to everyone; I figure that if the folks are interested, they'll ask. I don't do the "hard sell." But, when approached, I certainly will visit with the folks.

As I listened to the other authors explain what was going on, and that we were all selling our writings, a lady approached me.

"Are these your books?" she asked.

"Yes," I replied. I volunteered the information about the books.

"I'd like to buy them if you'll sign them," she said.

"That's fine," I said. "But what if I give you the books and charge you for the signature?"

The comment seemed to go over the lady's head. "Make it out to me," she said.

"I can do that," I said. "But do you know that the signature is worth more than the book?"

I got the gal's name and started to personalize a book for her.

"Do you mind if I take your picture?" she asked. "We had driven by and saw you, and had to turn around and come in. You looked just like a statue. You looked so lifelike."

"A statue," I said. "You know lady, I might be old and near death, but rigor mortis ain't even set in yet!"

Making Amends

My middle son, Sam, was working for me in Grand Lake, Colorado, one summer. I forget just how old he was at the time, probably only thirteen or fourteen, but he wasn't old enough to drive. There was another youngster there that summer about the same age as Sam.

This was a situation that was giving me some consternation, as these boys were constantly getting into trouble, most of it minor, but still trouble. The old saying about having one boy, you've got a pretty good worker, but when you have two boys, you've only got half a worker was proving itself true. The situation came to a head one night while I was at a meeting in Granby, about sixteen miles south.

When I got home after the meeting, I was surprised to find a couple of Grand County sheriff deputies at the house. As I got the details of the incident, it seems like the boys had decided to use the company pickup and do a little joy riding around the town. When they were pulled over, they couldn't produce a driver's license, so they had committed a crime. The deputies gave me some options; I could press charges for vehicular theft and let the boys spend some time in jail, or they could release the boys in my custody and forget the whole thing.

I chose the latter option, thinking that I might not be able to find the time to go to court, or the money to hire a lawyer. But I would have to determine a punishment that was suitable.

I decided to let the one boy go. I called his dad, told him the situation, and asked him to come and get the boy. He showed up and took his son home.

But Sam was another problem. I didn't know how to handle this situation. After some serious thought, I decided on the same action my own father had used on me—a trip to the woodshed, with a wide leather belt used on the bare bottom. And that's what I did.

That was the only time I felt compelled to discipline any of my kids in that manner. As the years passed, the thought of my actions that day weighed heavily on me, and I actually began to feel somewhat guilty about how I had handled the situation. I decided that I should try to make amends, not so much for Sam's sake, but for my own peace of mind.

When Sam had matured and was in his middle twenties, I decided to make my amends. At a family reunion, I pulled Sam aside, where we could talk privately.

I said, "Do you remember some years ago, when you an' that other kid stole the company truck an' went joy ridin' in Grand Lake?" He nodded. "Do you also remember that I gave you a pretty good whippin' for it?"

"Yes, I remember," he said.

"Well," I continued, "I've always felt kinda guilty about that. I need to kinda make things right with you."

"Don't worry about it. It worked," Sam said.

"What do you mean, don't worry about it?"

"It worked, Dad," was Sam's reply. "I never stole another truck!"

Forgetfulness?

My granddaughter, Jade, I guess she was about seven at the time, came up to Granby, Colorado, to go skiing with me. There was a catch in this deal; I had to drive Jade and her mom back to their home in Loveland, Colorado.

It's about 120 miles to Loveland, and Jade was getting a little bored and a little cranky.

"Tell me a joke, Jade," I said, trying to make the situation a little easier.

"I don't know any jokes," said Jade. "You tell me one, Grandpa."

"I don't really know any jokes that I can tell you," I said. "How's about I tell you a true story that might be kinda funny?"

"That would be kinda neat!"

"You know," I said, "I have false teeth. Well, I had these teeth in my mouth one day and they started hurting me. It really was painful. So, I took my teeth out and immediately felt better. They didn't hurt me anymore. I felt pretty good. I didn't know what to do with my teeth, so I put them in my back pocket. I forgot all about them until I went over and sat down in the truck ... and bit myself in the butt!"

This brought a good laugh from Jade and her mom, too!

About every fifteen or twenty miles, Jade would shake her head and say, "Bit myself in the butt," and laugh. It made for a better trip home.

A Profession?

Sometimes I'm at a loss to figure out what a person's goals are in life. I worked with a guy in Wyoming who didn't seem to have any goals at all. He would work for a few months, save a little bundle of money, then go get drunk and be content to take a cardboard sign and stand on a corner and beg for money.

I worked with him for two summers, and the second summer, when he showed up, he had a little knapsack with a change of clothes in it. That's all he owned. He also had a cardboard sign; I forget exactly what it said, but it was a request for money. If I remember it right, it said something like:

VETERAN
NEED HELP
PLEASE

"It's a good sign, I'm keeping it for future use," was his comment as he carefully placed it under his bed. According to him, he made a lot of money with that sign.

I constantly see other people on street corners or out in the median of exit- or on-ramps to freeways with their signs. I'd be interested in knowing just how much money they successfully beg every day, and if they pay taxes on it.

I'd also like to know if there are any arguments over preferred positions, or if some street corners are better than others.

There's a store in a downtown area that I frequent quite often, and I don't think there's ever been a time when I've walked into that store when someone hasn't approached me, wanting to bum a smoke or a dollar. I don't give money or anything else to street beggars, but I would like to give them a haircut. No, I wouldn't give them money for a haircut; I'd like to personally give them a haircut!

I don't think these people want a job—they have made a profession out of begging.

One time, I almost gave one of these beggars some money. His sign read:

WHY LIE?
I JUST WANT BEER

I thought his approach, though perhaps honest, was a bit unusual. I think of him every time I see one of these beggars, and wonder how much money he actually got with his honest approach.

Returning Borrowed Goods

I really hate to borrow stuff. When I return it, I generally have to borrow it back at a later date. I sometimes think it would be easier to keep it, in effect steal it, rather than return it and keep borrowing it, or just go out and buy the item myself.

I borrowed something one spring from a neighbor some years ago, and when I returned it in the fall, I felt kinda guilty. I had kept it longer than I had intended, even though I didn't use it every day. I certainly didn't want John to think I was trying to steal the item, and I wanted him to know that I really appreciated being able to keep and use it all summer.

"I really feel funny about returning this to you so long after I borrowed it," I said. "Maybe I can make it right with you. What kind of beer do you drink?" I thought I might get off easy with a six-pack of beer for him.

"I don't really drink much beer," replied John. "But I really do like vodka!"

I ended up paying quite a bit more for a fifth of vodka than I would have paid for a six-pack of beer, but I bought him a fifth, and resolved to not borrow anything from him again. Maybe he knew what he was doing!

I don't like to lend things out, either. I have never figured out how to profit on such dealings as John apparently has. However, I don't mind giving stuff away, if I'm done with it.

I TEACH SKIING in the winter and I have a lot of fun doing it. My students generally have a lot of fun learning how to ski. But there is one aspect of skiing that isn't much fun. For some reason or another, it seems like the cold weather is always accompanied by runny noses!

I had a woman in ski class that was struggling with both—learning how to ski and a runny nose. I always keep a bunch of napkins in one of my ski uniform pockets; I steal them from the cafeteria at meal times. They come in handy for me and my students.

Watching this woman try to perform each exercise to learn how to ski and control her nose at the same time was interesting. I would give her advice on what to do with her skis to achieve the desired result, but I think what she appreciated most was when I let her borrow a handful of napkins to help with her runny nose.

Her skiing got better as the day progressed, and by the end of the lesson she was linking turns together down the bunny hill. That's pretty good for a person who has never been on skis before.

We dismissed the class and I went to the locker room to change clothes and go home. As I crossed the patio by the lodge to leave, I heard someone calling my name.

"Stu! Stu!" It was the woman with the runny nose.

"I just wanted to thank you for teaching me how to ski," said the woman.

"You did a good job," said her husband, who was sitting nearby. "You actually taught her how to ski!"

"I also wanted to give you this," said the woman, reaching into her pocket. She pulled out a napkin from her pocket and started to hand it to me.

I saw what it was, and said, "Now wait a minute, lady. Those things are free and they're disposable! You don't have to return them!"

"But I want you to have it. It was so kind of you to lend it to me," she said.

"I really don't need it," I said. "Actually, I stole them from the cafeteria. You're really the recipient of stolen merchandise!"

"I don't care," she said, "I really want you to have it!"

"Listen, lady, I really don't need it. What am I going to do with a used napkin anyway?"

The lady's husband was watching from his chair with an amused look on his face.

As the woman reached for my hand to place the napkin in it, I instinctively pulled back. *What was she trying to do?*

"I think you better take that," said the husband. The amused look was still on his face, but the tone of his voice was very solemn. "And you ought to open it up before you throw it away!"

I took the napkin, very carefully. "What do I need with a used napkin? Your honesty is very apparent lady, but you don't have to do this."

"Open it," she said.

Cautiously, not knowing what to expect—and expecting the worst, I took the napkin. Even more cautiously, I opened it up.

I sure was surprised by the contents of the napkin. It was not filled with what I expected; inside the carefully folded napkin was a hundred dollar bill!

The surprised look on my face must have really amused the lady's husband ... he was enjoying a good laugh.

"We just wanted you to know how much we appreciate you teaching her how to ski!"

"That's just part of the job," I said. "This is unnecessary."

"You keep it. You earned it."

"I appreciate it," I said, "but this must be the most expensive napkin you ever borrowed!"

Do People Know
What They're Doing?

When I'm out selling my books, traveling from town to town, I sometimes get a little lonely. So, when I get to a bookstore, I'm looking to relax, and even have a little fun. If I can be relaxed, and enjoy my time with the store owner or managers, book sales are generally better and I feel better about driving down the road to the next town.

I really enjoy the personal contact with the management people, and I usually have a good time joking and fooling around with these folks. Sometimes I feel like the people I'm joking with don't realize they're actually buying books! And, I often wonder, when their payments are late, if they know they're supposed to send me a check! Maybe we carry the fun a little too far.

I was in a good mood when I approached the manager of one bookstore and made my sales pitch.

"I'd like to carry your books," said the manager, "but we're a little short of cash right now."

"When could you pay me?" I asked. I wanted to make a sale, and quite often in order to make a sale, I would have to extend credit for thirty days, sometimes more.

"We couldn't get you a check until February," she replied.

"We could do that," I replied. Then, I added, "If you remember to pay me!"

I grinned when I said that, but she shot me a dirty look, like she was thinking, *Don't you think we pay our bills?*

I really hadn't intended any sort of implication with that comment; I was just having a little fun. But I was a little concerned about extending credit until February. That was more like 120 days rather than the normal thirty days, and the possibility of my invoice getting lost or misplaced was a concern.

But, we went ahead and made the deal, making the bill payable February 2. I left the store feeling confident that a check would be in the mail by February, and didn't think much about it—until February.

February 2 rolled around and I hadn't received a check. I assumed it was in the mail; after all, the woman seemed quite insulted when I jokingly said, "If you remember to pay me!" Surely, she thought too highly of her business and herself to neglect a bill.

On the twentieth of February I decided to give her a call and rattle her chain. More than four months had passed and her bill was almost three weeks late. I got to wondering if my invoice had been lost, misplaced, or forgotten. Yes, I was becoming a little concerned, and even though $111.00 wouldn't make or break me, it was the principle of the matter. There had been plenty of time to write a check, and there was a sentence on the bottom of my invoice to her that read, "Service fee of 10% per month will be added to all past due accounts."

I really thought I could prompt her payment with a call, and maybe save her eleven bucks in the process. Even though I hadn't seen or talked with her for more than four months, I knew I got the manager of the store by the curt manner in which she answered the phone. She sounded very perturbed.

I introduced myself and told her that she had a past due bill, and it was getting close to being a month overdue. I mentioned the 10 percent statement on the invoice.

Very curtly, she said, "The woman who writes the checks has your invoice. You will receive a check next week, Mister Campbell!"

I thought to myself, *Your telephone skills could use some improving.* I thanked her for her attention to the matter, and she hung up!

As I write this, I am sure I will get paid sometime ... I just don't know when.

On that particular bookselling trip, in that particular part of that particular state, I sold quite a few books. But I ended up with four accounts that were more than thirty days late in paying me, and one of the checks bounced. I don't think I'll return to that particular part of that particular state trying to sell books and extend any credit!

Perception

Teaching skiing to beginning skiers can sometimes be very amusing. Students can easily get confused about what they have to do to turn in a given direction. Quite often I've had to give instructions on how to turn left only to have the student turn right. These situations are mostly humorous to me, but also very frustrating.

When this happens, I've been known to holler at my students, "No! No! Your other left!"

This will almost always bring a grin from the student and a more concentrated effort to perform the exercise properly. I'm sure part of the confusion stems from the fact that when I'm facing the student, my right side is the student's left. To help ensure understanding, I will demonstrate on my right foot what the student is supposed to do with his left foot. This seems to help, as most people are visual learners. But it's still confusing.

Often, to help alleviate confusion, I will turn my back to the students and demonstrate with my left foot what they're supposed to do with their left foot. While doing this, I will ask the question, "Do you think that if I put all my weight on my right foot and tip to the outside edge of my left ski, like this—will I turn left?" As I ask the question, I demonstrate exactly what I'm saying.

I'm not concerned with their answers; I'm prepared to show that it will work.

I had a class of five or six adult students, all of them beginners. We were on the easiest of all the slopes, and a person had to really work in order to slide down the incline. It was a real gentle slope.

The students were lined up, ready to make their attempts to turn left.

"I'm going to turn my back to you and ask you a question," I said.

I turned around and started to resume my dialog. "Do you think ...?"

I never got a chance to finish the question. With my back turned to my students, I was interrupted.

"The question is," said a lady, "do you think these pants make my butt look big?"

I was caught totally unprepared, and after the woman's comment, I found it difficult to immediately continue the class. The other members of the class broke out in a big laugh. We did continue the class when I regained my composure, although I did have to take a few minutes to stop laughing.

It was a fun day.

A Free Pass!

Occasionally, I'm asked to do some public speaking at various conferences or conventions. I generally accept these invitations simply because it's an honor to be asked, and the people asking me provide a motel room and meals. It's an opportunity to do some traveling and see different parts of the country.

A few years ago, I was asked to speak at a conference in Vernal, Utah. I was looking forward to this speaking engagement, as I had lived in the area some years before and had a few good friends there.

John Anderson had become a good friend over the years, although I didn't like him when I first met him. John was a lawyer and had represented my first wife during our divorce, so there was a natural animosity towards him right from the start. Over the years my animosity had mellowed, my attitude had changed and we had become good friends.

Over the years, John had become active in civic affairs and had become a judge. I have a brother-in-law who is also a judge in Salt Lake City, and although I am somewhat of a black sheep in the company of these two esteemed gentlemen, I feel very fortunate that I have not had to appear in either one of their courtrooms!

The day before my speaking engagement in Vernal, I met John as he was leaving a rodeo committee meeting. I said to him, "Are you signing up for the bronc riding? You might be a little old for that, John."

"No," said John. "I'm on the committee. I understand you're going to speak tomorrow night."

"That's correct," I replied. "Are you going to be there?"

"Yes," answered John. "Are you going to be there?"

"I expect to be there, John. Only death or jail will prohibit me from being there," I quipped.

"Well," replied John, "I can handle the jail part!"

I didn't realize it at the time, but I had been given a "Get Out of Jail Free" card—a free pass! Fortunately, I didn't have to use it.

Out of My Class

My brother Jim lives in Henderson, Nevada. A couple of times during the year on my book selling trips, I can swing through Henderson, visit with Jim, play some golf with him, and have him do some work on my computer. I'm computer illiterate and Jim can set up spreadsheets, formulas, and everything I need. I can punch in the numbers in the appropriate columns when everything is set up.

Jim's wife, Carolyn, had given him a year's membership to a somewhat exclusive golf club near Henderson, and Jim had set us up with a tee time. I put my clubs in Jim's car and we started out to the golf course.

My expectations were quite simple—just have a good day golfing with my brother. I didn't expect to improve my game; I think it's as good as it will ever be. No, I'm not that good; I have reached the pinnacle of mediocrity and can't expect to improve much. A couple of pars, a couple of bogies are about all I can expect, and I'm satisfied. If I get a birdie, I've had an excellent day.

Jim got us to the golf course; I took my clubs out of the car and proceeded to put on my golf shoes. Golf course management doesn't appreciate high-heeled cowboy boots walking on their manicured greens. I got my shoes tied, after some difficulty. My golf shoes are the only "tie-up" shoes I own.

I went to get my golf clubs ... and they were gone! Somebody had stolen my golf clubs!

I hurriedly looked around searching for my missing clubs and possibly even the culprit. I saw my clubs and Jim's being carried toward the clubhouse.

"Hey! Hold it right there!" I was hurrying to retrieve my stolen clubs. "I'll take those," I hollered.

Jim seemed a little alarmed. "Stu, he's just doing his job. He'll carry the clubs to the clubhouse for us!"

"Oh," I said. "The courses where I play, I could sit in the truck all day waiting for someone to carry my clubs, an' nobody would show up."

"This is a very exclusive golf club," said Jim.

"There you are, Mister Campbell," said the young man I thought was stealing our clubs. He placed the clubs in a cart.

Mister Campbell, I thought, *that's Jim, my brother ... younger brother at that! Mister Campbell is our dad! This is more exclusive than what I'm used to!*

Jim tipped the guy a couple of bucks and went into the clubhouse. I sat in the cart guarding our clubs. I have to admit, I wasn't sure just how this deal worked.

We played our golf game and had a good day. Jim beat me, miserably, much to his delight.

Jim went to the clubhouse and I started to clean the cart of pop bottles and the mess.

"I'll do that, sir." It was the young man I thought was stealing our clubs earlier.

"No, I can handle it," I said.

"I'll take your clubs," he said.

"No, I can do that," I said. I was still suspicious and didn't want my clubs stolen.

"But I'm supposed to take your clubs, clean them, and put them in your car. That's my job. That's what I'm paid for."

"Well," I said, "Take Jim's, that is, Mister Campbell's, an' do what you have to do. I'll take care of my own equipment."

"Yes sir," said the young man. He looked a little disheartened.

"That's how you make a living?" I asked.

"Yes sir," replied the young man.

"Well," I said, "I'll make you a deal. How's about I clean my clubs an' you give me ten bucks?"

Jim returned and we put my clubs in his car. Presently, the young man returned with Jim's clubs. Jim gave him a tip and we left.

I think I know why, and Jim has never mentioned it, but in subsequent years Jim hasn't taken me to that golf club again. I'd like to think it's because he was afraid I'd beat him at his fancy club, but I have a sneaking suspicion there may be other reasons.

Working Too Hard

I have some grandkids in Salt Lake City, Utah, and only get to see them about twice a year. I really look forward to seeing them and have a lot of fun when we do get together.

However, the grandkids are in school during the week, and my kids are working, so I don't have a lot to do while I'm visiting. I tried playing some golf, but it became a little too expensive.

Then I came across a little executive golf course that was kinda fun and inexpensive. At the time, they only charged ten dollars for nine holes, with a cart. That was their senior rate. I thought the price was reasonable, so I played eighteen holes for twenty dollars.

I wasn't too pleased with my game, so I decided to play some more. The guys in the club house looked at me kinda strange when I said, "I wasn't too pleased with my game, so I better go again."

"That can certainly be arranged," the reply came a little apprehensively. The strange look was still on everyone's faces.

"How come you're givin' me those strange looks?" I asked.

"Most people only play eighteen, and then stop."

"Well," I said, "I ain't got nothin' else to do. Besides that, I'm used to workin' fifteen to eighteen hours a day, so don't give me any of your crap for having fun for ten hours!"

"Mister Campbell, if that's your attitude, the rest of the golf you play today will be absolutely free!"

That day I played 54 holes of golf for twenty dollars. And I played 54 holes the next day for twenty dollars a day. Unfortunately, my golf score didn't improve much, despite the monetary savings.

Now I've played that course so much, people are wondering if I'm going to Salt Lake City to play golf or to visit my grandkids. Sometimes, I'm not too sure myself!

Hunt and Peck

Quite often, when I'm out on the road selling my books, I'll have to spend an extra day in a motel. Most of the time this happens on a Sunday, and I can watch the football games in the fall and relax some. Occasionally, I have to spend an extra weekday due to truck problems or whatever.

Such was the case in Riverton, Wyoming, in the fall of 2010. My truck needed some repair that would take a full day. I found a motel with a fairly reasonable rate right across the road from the repair shop, and settled in to try and wait patiently for my truck to be repaired. Then I found out that the work on my truck couldn't be completed in one day and it would take most of the next day to finish it up, so I had to spend an extra day.

The next day, I checked on the truck. It would take most of the day to complete, so I settled down in the motel with a cup of coffee to work on my writing.

I was involved in my typing when I heard a knock on the door. I was so involved that the knock startled me. I opened the door. It was the maids.

"Do you need maid service?"

"If you want to make the bed, that would be alright," I answered. "Do you want me to leave? I'm doing some work on my computer."

"No, that's okay."

I resumed my writing as the maids started their work. Typing for me is a chore; however, a computer makes it easier. Using a typewriter, I can do about twenty words a minute, not counting the time it takes to erase a misspelled word, or replace the paper because I've erased through it. With the computer, I can correct my mistakes with a touch or two of a button. But it still takes time.

"What are you working on?" One of the maids was curious.

"Well," I replied, "I've written three books an' I'm workin' on another one. I have to wait for my truck to be fixed, so I figured I'd try to do something constructive an' make the most of my idle time."

"We've met a rich and famous author," said one of the maids.

"You're only about half right on each count," I replied. "I'm certainly not rich an' I sure ain't famous."

"But I don't know that I've ever met an author before," said one of the maids.

"This room certainly isn't dirty," said the other maid.

"Generally, it takes me more than one day to make a good mess," I said, ignoring the reference to being rich and famous. I resumed my typing, using one finger, occasionally using two when I had to.

"You hunt and peck," said the maid, observing my concentration and style at the computer.

"Once again, you're only about half right," I said. Without thinking, I continued, "I do know where all the keys are on the typewriter, but it's a little different on the computer ... there are some extra keys. I don't have to hunt so much, so you might say I'm more of a pecker!"

"You said it!" replied one of the maids.

As the maids were going out the door, laughing, one of them said, "Have a good day, Mister Pecker!

Coincidence

I frequent a few special interest clubs when I'm on the road. I've been to some of them often enough that I've gotten to know quite a few people there and have made some good friends. I'm always anxious to see who is still around when I show up.

I showed up one night at a club in Salt Lake City, Utah. After a short visit with some old timers, I went to my son's house to get good night's sleep. I had driven almost 500 miles that day and thought I could use some rest.

The next morning, I got up early and went to the club to get some coffee and continue visiting with old friends. I was somewhat surprised to see yellow tape tied to the front of the building, blocking off one of the doors to the building.

"What happened?" I asked, after going inside.

"We were broken into last night or early this morning," answered Ronnie, as he poured my coffee. "All they stole was the cash register. They didn't get any money. They broke the window and went straight to the cash register. They must have been nuts. They went right over the computer to the cash register and left the computer."

"That's too bad," I said, as I paid for my coffee and went to join some friends seated at a table nearby.

The conversation at the table was primarily about the robbery the night before. All sorts of theories were stated about who did it and why.

Finally, Kenny said, "It's a real coincidence that Stu showed up last night and then we were robbed."

I had known Kenny for years and knew he was just kidding. I decided to go along with it.

"What did they get?" I asked.

"Nothing really. Just ..."

I interrupted Kenny. "That *is* a real coincidence," I said.

"How come?"

"That's a real coincidence because I ain't got *nothing!*"

Fortunately, Kenny was only kidding and I got away without having to make a trip to the police station, but it was too bad they had their stuff stolen.

Travel Tips

I watch with great interest the morning television shows, particularly in the spring when people are planning their summer vacations. I watch because I do a lot of traveling in the spring and fall, and I'd like to see if I could make my travels easier.

Some of the travel tips they give out are fairly obvious, like call ahead for reservations, take some extra gas, make sure there's a good reserve on the credit card balance, have the car maintained and the oil changed.

However, I think they miss the boat in a lot of instances. They never mention important stuff, like taking along an extra set of car keys—and keeping them in an unused pocket, not inside the car. It doesn't do much good to have an extra set of keys locked inside the car along with the keys that are regularly used locked inside with them.

The most important thing I feel the talk-show hosts or travel experts leave out is probably never considered by the most intelligent of travelers. I never leave on a trip without one. They are inexpensive, don't take up much room, and are easy to carry. It's a flyswatter!

This valuable little device has led to many comfortable evenings while relaxing in a motel room—trouble-free evenings if they are used properly.

I've noticed that motel rooms seem to harbor flies in the spring and the fall. I presume it's because the maids leave the doors open while they're cleaning the rooms. This is an open invitation to a fly to get in out of the heat or the cold, or to just stop in to investigate.

I've entered some rooms and have been immediately greeted by flies. Sometimes the greeting is so enthusiastic I feel that the flies have been locked up for days and are longing for some companionship—someone to talk to. Often, the flies will hover right in front of my face, like they're telling a long lost secret.

To me, these pesky little devils are a real nuisance. Until I started carrying a flyswatter, I was constantly interrupting my work to brush them away. At times I felt like I was being attacked! The flyswatter has solved the problem and enabled me to take control of my temporary world in the motel.

Now, I enter a motel room with weapon in hand—ready to defend my right to serenity. Much like an old-time cowboy in an old "B" western movie entering a saloon full of bad guys, I boldly walk in the room looking for the bad flies. The hunt is on. I carefully scrutinize all the walls, the ceilings, and the countertops. No mercy is shown when the enemy is located. They are promptly disposed of wherever their location. They are left where they fall; it's the maid's job to clean up the room!

After my initial investigation is completed, I can begin my work, uninterrupted. But my weapon is always close by. These pesky little devils are cunning, and quite often hide out until conditions are appropriate for their emergence, namely when the room warms up.

Carrying a flyswatter has been one of the most useful items I can take on a trip. I always make sure there is one in my vehicle when I leave on one.

Candy?

Sometimes I'll get some candy to munch on in between meals. I used to worry about gaining some weight, but I don't worry about it anymore. I haven't gained weight for the last twenty or thirty years. I used to worry about my teeth, but I don't worry anymore; I've had false teeth for the last twenty some odd years. So there's not much to worry about and I generally have something to chew on.

When I retired sometime in 2000, I thought I would play a lot of golf and do a lot of skiing. However, I can't afford to ski as much as I'd like to. I found out that when you're a ski instructor, you get a season pass for free. Consequently, I became a ski instructor.

Wanting to chew on something while teaching skiing, and not wanting to chew tobacco because constantly spitting that brown stuff on the white snow becomes unsightly, and the tobacco gets stuck between my dentures and my gums, I started carrying some candy with me. This presented somewhat of a problem because I was reluctant to bring it out in front of eight or ten students without sharing. Quite often, I didn't bring enough to share with everyone.

I became quite fond of the candy Good and Plenty. This is a licorice candy, coated with a sugar shell. It comes in two colors, pink and white. The uniformity of the candy makes it resemble prescription pills.

I shared quite a bit of this candy with students, pouring it out of the box to outstretched gloved hands. This resulted in a lot of spillage and me not getting the full benefit of the snack.

———

TEACHING SKIING can quite often be frustrating. I wonder if students are so concerned with not falling that they miss the point of the instruction. Some of my students have noticed this, and commented that, "Teaching skiing must be very difficult," or "This must be very frustrating for you."

It is frustrating, until the lesson starts to come together for the student. I try not to show my frustration to the student.

One day, during a particularly difficult class when I was popping some Good and Plenty candy into my mouth, a student noticed it. Apparently she hadn't noticed the box I'd gotten the candy from.

"Are you taking medication?"

The question was simple enough. Without thinking, I answered, "Yes."

"What for?" she asked.

I had started something. "It's nothing serious, just some heart medication with some pain killers and tranquilizers."

"Are you supposed to take a handful at a time?"

"No," I answered, "just one. But if one is good, ten or twelve ought to be ten or twelve times better, shouldn't it?"

"I don't know," she answered.

We continued the ski lesson, but I noticed the lady was watching me, closer than the other students. At the conclusion of the lesson, noting the lady's concern, I approached her.

"You've been watching me very closely, lady."

"Yes," she said. "I'm a nurse and I was looking for an adverse reaction to all that medication you took all at one time. Abuse of medications is very common these days and ..."

I interrupted her. "This isn't really medication. Actually, it's candy!'

I pulled the box out of my coat. "Here, do you want some?" I offered the box to her.

"No," she said, visibly relieved. But I suspected she really didn't believe me.

However, she did give me an idea.

That night at the house, I got an old aspirin bottle, tore off the label, and filled it with Good and Plenty candy.

The next day during class, I rode the lift with some students. I got out the aspirin bottle and poured about half the contents into my hand, making sure the students riding with me could see the "pills" in my hand.

"What's that?" one of the students asked.

"Tranquilizers," I replied.

"Are you supposed to take so many?"

"No. But this has been a rough class and you people have frazzled my nerves! This is my relief!"

"We haven't been that bad!" It was obvious my students didn't fully believe my story.

"No," I said. "Worse!"

We had some fun that day.

Just Do It

Quite often I'm asked, "How did you get started writing?" The answer is kinda complicated. I always enjoyed writing in high school, as long as I could select the theme. I did have some fun with it.

In college, the English classes seemed to be full of writing assignments; themes, essays, and the like. Three-quarters of English class appeared to be preparation for writing a Master's thesis or a Doctorate. I really didn't have any plans to go on to higher education; math and chemistry had effectively lowered my grade point average enough that further education seemed pointless.

However, towards the end of my college career, I did take a creative writing class, just for the fun of it. I enjoyed the class, although my final grade didn't help my grade point average much. The professor thought

I had some good ideas, but he liked to cover my manuscripts with red ink for spelling and punctuation errors. He was also quite free in using the red pen to suggest alternative methods of saying something or carrying an idea further. He used so much red ink on my submissions that I often thought he might be a communist!

I also thought, because he was so free with his suggestions, that he was an unpublished author, and very frustrated. But he did give me good marks for my ideas. I decided that I would write actual stuff, fiction didn't really appeal to me.

———

WHILE WORKING ONE summer as a wrangler in the Grand Teton National Park, I got real tired of listening to a co-worker. As Pete Peterson worked with the dudes, answering questions, and watching their actions around the horses, his most common remark was, "I ought to write a book!"

He said that so often that I began to wonder, *Why don't you just do it?* I actually suggested to him that he should write a book, just to get him to stop repeat-ing himself. I don't know if he actually took my suggestion, but after a summer of listening to him, I decided that I would never continually use a phrase like that without doing something about it.

Some years later, I was reading a supposedly humorous article in a horse magazine. Upon completing the article, I threw the magazine on the floor in disgust.

"What's wrong?" My wife was not used to seeing such outbursts from me.

"This is a lousy article," I replied. "I could do better myself!"

"Why don't you just do it?"

Somewhat angered and upset with my wife's simple reply, I went to the spare bedroom I had set up as an office, pulled out some paper and started to write. My first effort was a short story, titled "Rough String Rider."

I had the article all written out, nice and neat on college-ruled, three-ringed paper. Now, what to do with it?

Actually, I let the article sit for about three weeks. Fear of rejection prohibited me from sending the article to a magazine. Questions appeared in my mind, questions like, *Would they laugh at my submission?*

Frankly, they were supposed to laugh, it was a humorous article. But my mind would ask me, *Would they laugh at me for the wrong reasons?*

Finally, I put my fears aside, stopped my questioning mind, and timidly mailed my manuscript to the magazine. I remember thinking as I slipped the envelope, complete with return postage, into the mailbox, *They don't know me and I don't know them, so what can it hurt?*

Patiently, I waited for three days for a reply, and then anxiously checked the mail looking for some response. After about two weeks with no reply, I began to think that the magazine didn't think the manuscript was even worth returning.

Then, about a month after I originally mailed the article and when I had about given up, a letter appeared in the mailbox. It was from the magazine. Hastily and somewhat nervously, I went to the truck to open the letter. I wanted to open the letter in private; I didn't want the possibility of my rejection becoming public.

There wasn't a check in the envelope, but the letter said something to the effect that they "liked the article and wanted to use it in a future issue." They also wanted to know if it had been published before or if it had been sent to any other publications.

Of course the answer was no. Fear of rejection had prohibited my sending the article to more than one publication. I didn't want my embarrassment to be nationwide.

Hurriedly, I sent a reply that stated the article was theirs, if they wanted it. They had offered to buy the "first time, one time only" rights. Of course I would sell it, that's why I sent it in, to sell it, and to prove to my wife that I could do better.

I had no idea what they paid, but I began spending money like I had written a best seller. I also started writing a second article.

Some months later, I was disappointed when I received a check for $35.00 for my article. I thought I would make thousands of dollars, and had spent accordingly in celebration.

My first submission was sent to *Horseman Magazine*, and they accepted twenty some odd articles over a period of a couple of years before they rejected one. They even featured a few of my stories on the cover, although quite often I didn't initially recognize them—they had changed the title! That was all right with me, they kept sending me checks for the articles.

Their first rejection, while it was discouraging, came with some encouragement. It read something to the effect that, "This is a good article, and you can sell it to another magazine. We have a backlog of your articles; you're starting to have a following and we don't want to burn out our readers."

This rejection gave me permission to submit to other magazines, even though I wasn't under a contract with *Horseman Magazine*. But, *Horseman Magazine* had accepted my first submission and I felt somewhat loyal to them. Eventually, I had articles accepted by a number of magazines, including *Western Horseman, Horse Lover's, The Quarter Horse Journal,* and others.

Over the years, I sold quite a few articles to various magazines, always selling only "first time, one time rights." I accumulated a lot of stories that had already been published and felt quite successful.

It was time to do something with them again. I decided to see if I could sell a book. I took the manuscript to a book publisher in Salt Lake City, Utah, that published a few western books. After an initial glance, the publisher indicated that the book "showed promise."

I left the manuscript with him and returned home, consigned to waiting a considerable amount of time, but confident that I would soon be joining the ranks of Shakespeare, O'Henry, Mark Twain, Zane Gray, and others, possibly of biblical fame.

After a few months of waiting with no word, I was in Salt Lake City on some other business, and stopped in at the publisher to check on the progress of my manuscript. The publisher assured me that they were going to publish the book, they just didn't know when.

Feeling reassured, I left, envisioning a popular best selling book still possible. A year passed, with still no word from the publisher. I was used to waiting—most of the articles I'd sold were paid on publication rather than acceptance, so I was used to waiting, sometimes a considerable amount of time. But this was becoming ridiculous. I had proposed that the book be printed so I could make some money, but I hadn't made a dime.

Frustrated, I picked up the manuscript, and rather than submitting it to another publisher and wait a considerable amount of time, I decided to publish it myself. I had become upset and decided to just do it.

I selected a few stories, found a printer, got a picture for the cover and had my first book printed. It consisted of forty pages, paperback, held together with two staples. I titled it *Horsing Around*. I priced it modestly, knowing that the bookstores and saddle shops where I hoped to sell it would have to show a profit on it. I also hoped to show a profit. It sold for $4.50 per book.

The book did well enough, so I decided to do another one, this one called *More Horsing Around*. Eventually I ended up printing two more, *Still Horsing Around*, and *Just Horsing Around*. These little forty-page books did pretty well, but they presented the look of a forty-page pamphlet rather than a book. So, after some success with the four books, I decided to combine them into one book, 160 pages, perfect bound with a full-color cover, just like a real book.

The combined effort, *Horsing Around A Lot,* initially sold for $12.95, but before a second printing, and because of the economy, I raised the price to $15.95.

I decided to distribute the book myself, offering retail stores the same discounts that regular publishers offered. Distributors wanted too much of a discount, thereby cutting into my profit margin.

After a time, I found my retail outlet managers and owners asking, "When are you going to do a second one? We have some customers telling us that they enjoyed the first one and would like to see another one."

The question was asked often enough that it prompted work on a second book, *Horsin' Around the Dudes.* It came out in the fall of 2008, and was well accepted by my established retail outlets.

A third book, *Humor Around Horses,* came out in the fall of 2010. It appears that I have found a few more occupations—author, distributor, salesman, and general flunky for my writing efforts. Now, I work in the winter and summer, and take the spring and fall to take a long vacation, and pay for it at the same time by selling books.

I do enjoy it, although it does become somewhat tiresome driving around the country. I'm surprised at the number of miles that I put on the truck driving around a strange town looking for a bookstore, then looking for a parking spot. But I have been able to make it pay off, modestly.

It didn't come as a great surprise when I found out that my previous customers that had bought six of my first book ended up buying three each of my two books. When I got the third book, customers generally would not buy six of each, but would buy two of each. Six seems to be the magic number.

It all started with a challenge: "Why don't you just do it?"

Well, why not?

No Rest for the Wicked, or Even the Weary

Teaching skiing can be pretty tough sometimes. A ski instructor has to deal with a lot of different variables, from a student's fear of the slope, to a person who doesn't really want to be there. On the other end of the spectrum, there's the person that is gung-ho and willing to go for it, regardless of the consequences.

When the ski school has a lot of instructors, quite often an instructor can split the class so the students that are struggling can get some extra help, and those gung-ho students can proceed at an accelerated pace. This works out well when there are a lot of instructors, but when the ski school is short-handed, it becomes a struggle to do a good job of teaching with all the variable abilities of the students. I have seen instructors swap half their class with another instructor in order to accomplish the goal of teaching as many students as possible, and still end up with acceptable results.

Busy times of the ski season also present a problem. Typically, the busiest times of the season are those times before Christmas to New Year's Day, Martin Luther King's birthday, President's Day, and Spring Break in March.

I have never understood Spring Break. I didn't know anything about Spring Break until I got to college. I don't remember a Spring Break as a child; I thought Spring Break was a college holiday, available only to those that made it that far through school. Now, high schools and even elementary schools observe Spring Break.

March is when Spring Break occurs, and here in Colorado most of the snow comes in March and April. The one redeeming feature of March is that the daytime temperatures are generally getting warmer. But the lift lines are longer and the ski classes more crowded, and the runs are more crowded, too.

Except for the moderate temperatures, the same is true for the Christmas season. School is out a few days before Christmas and until the first Monday after New Year's Day, ski areas are generally packed plumb full.

Such was the case a few years ago during the holidays. To make matters worse, a considerable number of ski instructors had obtained additional time off to be with family and friends during the holidays. This made for a tough time for the remaining instructors—ski classes were overloaded with all sorts of abilities and desires. As the holidays slowly passed, it was easy to see severe fatigue engulfing the remaining instructors.

Toward the end of the holidays, most of the ski instructors were looking for the end, for a break. The return of those instructors that had obtained time off was eagerly anticipated, as it would relieve the pressure on the instructors that had stayed.

There was a noticeable difference in the parking lot the first Monday after New Year's Day. Compared to the previous ten days, the parking lot could almost be described as "vacant."

The "line-up," where instructors were assigned classes for the ski school, was the opposite. A lot of instructors were present, but not many students available.

"Where were you when we needed you?" The question was asked of all the instructors that had received time off. Also asked was as an obvious rib. "How was your vacation?"

Some of the instructors got so involved in answering the last question that they forgot why they were there.

I was one of the instructors that stayed behind during the holidays, and I have to admit that it wouldn't have bothered me if I didn't get a class. I was tired!

The director of the ski school asked one of the instructors returning from an extended stay with his family, "Are you ready to go back to work?"

The question was fair, but I was totally dismayed with the instructor's answer, as he said, "I've been off for ten days and haven't done any skiing at all. I'd like to have a day of free skiing!"

My thoughts of realizing some relief to the pressure vanished as I watched the instructor start to the lift to go play. I started to a group of beginning skiers to start my class and thought, *It's true there's no rest for the wicked!* But I couldn't think of anything wrong that I had done, and I started my class thinking, *There's no rest for the weary either!*

Perplexed

I sold a lot of my books to a dude rancher; if I remember right he was in Colorado, but his dude ranch could have been anywhere in the West. I was quite pleased that he'd bought about forty books, and that's a pretty large sale for me.

As I visited with this dude rancher, the thought occurred to me, *What is he going to do with all these books?* My intention in selling them to him was that he could resell them and make a few dollars and provide his guests with a souvenir of their visit. But forty books was quite a lot to have on hand.

The question kept nagging on me as we visited, and finally I asked him, "What are you going to do with all these books?"

"I'll sell them in our gift shop," he replied. "What we don't sell, I'll send out to our previous guests."

I was satisfied with this answer and content. As a salesman for my books, I feel like I've done my retail outlets a disservice if I overstock them. I want to be careful with such matters so I can go back in the future and sell them more books.

Yes, I was satisfied with his answer until a few days later, after I had given the situation some thought. The dude rancher hadn't told me if he was going to send what he didn't sell to his customers that he wanted to come back, or to those he didn't!

I'm still perplexed!

Proper Demonstrations

Quite often at the ski area where I spend the winter, we are short of ski instructors during the busy times of the ski season. When a few of the hosts, individuals that had volunteered to ski around the mountain and assist guests, indicated an interest in becoming ski instructors, they were more than welcomed.

Some training was done for these new instructors, mainly in accompanying a class to watch and learn the procedures we use in teaching beginning skiers. I was fortunate in having Sandra "shadow" my class to learn the process.

Sandra was a nice, middle-aged lady, already an accomplished skier. As our lesson progressed, I began to use her to demonstrate some of the movements used in parallel skiing to the students. This went fairly well; however, Sandra was an experienced skier and skied with her feet parallel, but really close together.

This made it difficult for the students to see what she was doing with her feet to accomplish the movements.

We took a break from our lesson and I got Sandra aside, privately.

"How is our lesson going?" I asked. "Are we making progress with our students? Do you think they will actually be able to ski when we get done?" I was curious to see what her reaction to our teaching methods was.

"I think they're really doing well," she replied. "Am I doing my demonstrations well enough?"

"Your demonstrations are good enough, however, you need to exaggerate your movements so the students can see what you're doing and observe the results you are getting. Remember, most people are visual learners and even though we tell them what to do, when they see what we are doing and see the results we are getting, it makes it easier for them to achieve the results we want."

"So, how do I do that?"

"Well," I replied, "You're already an accomplished skier, so you need to concentrate on showing the beginning skiers the movements you are doing to get the results you want. The best way to do this is to move your feet farther apart. When your feet are close together as they are when you ski normally, the student can't see clearly the tipping motion you are using to initiate the turn. If you spread your feet apart, the student can see your movements more clearly. I have to consciously think about this when I'm doing demonstrations."

Sandra gave the idea some thought, and then said, "That makes sense. But there seems to be something not entirely correct in telling a woman my age to spread her legs!"

She caught me by surprise, but we both had a good laugh over her comment.

"Remember," I said, "we're only teaching skiing here!"

A Positive Error

Teaching skiing can be a very trying experience. Invariably people that are trying to learn how to ski become confused and start to turn right rather than left, and visa-versa. Sometimes this situation can become kinda humorous, and I take particular delight in correcting my students.

"No! No! Your other right," is a common admonition to beginning ski students. I first heard this phrase in the army when the drill instructors were teaching raw recruits close-order drill. Eventually, most students get straightened out and actually begin to ski.

For me, generally the hardest students to teach are high school age students. A lot of high schools and churches will bring their teenagers to the ski areas for a weekend or week of winter recreation. Quite often these organizations are located in the South, where they don't have the opportunity to participate in snow sports, so they obviously need some instruction.

I find that a lot of these teenagers really don't have an interest in learning how to ski—they'd rather go snowmobiling or sledding and are only in the ski class because their chaperones have signed them up. And, even though they might want to learn how to ski, they are easily distracted. Invariably, the boys are watching the girls and the girls are watching the boys. They are not paying attention to their ski instructor.

I remember one particularly difficult class. These individuals all had a hard time differentiating right from left. I began to think it was me, but I carefully reviewed my instructions and demonstrations and it wasn't me. I was just having a hard time getting through to these kids, probably due to the competition from the opposite sexes.

I was also concerned because I understood that this particular high school graduated all their students, and something like 95 to 99 percent of their students went on to college, and many of them went on to obtain a Master's or Doctorate degree.

After what seemed like a very trying two-hour lesson that I thought would never end, the lesson was over. Some of the students had made some progress, but many needed more work. I thought it would be a good idea if I went to their chaperones and told them what each student needed to work on to become a better skier. I also thought it would it would be a good idea to do this in a humorous manner.

I found the chaperones in the cafeteria having lunch.

"I would like to tell you folks what each one of my student's needs to work on to improve their skiing," I said.

The chaperones seemed to appreciate this idea.

"Some of the students are having a hard time going to the right when they're told to. Very consistently, they're going left when they're told to go right. So," I continued, "I think it would be a good idea if the Florida Department of Education would teach their students the difference between right and left!"

I continued on, naming each student in my class and what each one needed to do to improve their skiing. The chaperones listened as I continued. "You might encourage these kids to work on these things as they ski."

I concluded my presentation, thinking I had done my students a great service, and got my own lunch. While I was eating, I did notice my boss, the director of the ski school, talking with the chaperones. When my boss left the chaperones, he came over to where I was eating.

"I need to see you in my office after lunch," he said.

"You bet!"

I went to the ski school office after lunch, thinking I was going to receive a compliment on what a fine job I had done. It had been a very difficult class, with issues not only between right and left, but there had been some balance and coordination issues, also. I really thought I had done an exceptional job with this class.

"We've had a complaint about you."

This session was not starting out as I had envisioned.

"What seems to be the problem?" I asked.

My boss explained to me that the chaperones had taken exception to my comment about the Florida Department of Education needing to teach their students the difference between left and right, and that this was a very exceptional school setting, which achieved very high academic standards.

I explained to him that I had tried to pinpoint to the chaperones one particular aspect that each student needed to work on, and had tried to preface my comments with some humor.

"They didn't think it was very funny," my boss replied.

"Perhaps," I replied, "the Florida Department of Education needs to teach their students and staff something about a sense of humor!"

Yes, I guess I did wrong, and was reprimanded for it. However, the positive results of this experience were far reaching. I have *not* had to teach a group of teenagers since that day! Had I known my comments would have had such results, I would have said them years earlier!

Book Signings

Publishing a new book and putting it out in bookstores or wherever it might sell can be frustrating. I haven't really done any advertising, as I'm generally not in one spot long enough to reply to inquiries. I don't rely on book distributors; they generally want a bigger cut of any income that might result. And why should I use them when I can give retail outlets the same discounts that publishers give and retain more for myself? This might even result in a profit for me. After all, I've incurred all the costs of publication—cover design, editing, and layout—so I need to make a profit.

Also, if I distribute the books, it gives me an opportunity to personally meet the people I'm dealing with. Plus, it gives me an opportunity to take a vacation and pay for it at the same time. Now that's really cheap, but to me it makes sense.

One way to attract some interest in a new book is to set up a book signing. I've always kinda enjoyed these affairs, but only schedule them when I know I'm going to be in the area. It doesn't make sense to drive a couple hundred miles only to sell a few books.

One time, I set up a book signing in northern Wyoming. Through cooperation between bookstore owners in various Wyoming towns, we managed to set up signings in a different store in a different town each day for five days. Even though one bookstore owner forgot to advertise the event, over the course of the five days, I managed to sell enough books to cover motels, gas, and meals on the five-day trip. I'm sure I could have done better if I was a famous movie star or some other sort of celebrity. But that's all right.

Of course, not all book signings are successful, but a person doesn't know that until he does them. Some are more successful than others. Most of the time they are successful enough to cover the costs incurred.

However, one instance comes to mind when I didn't cover any costs and didn't sell any books.

We had set up a book-signing event and had allowed plenty of time for the store owner to have the books reviewed, the reviews published, and the event advertised. As it turned out, I left for the town a day early as it was winter and some pretty heavy snowstorms were in the weather forecast. I was prepared to spend an extra day in case the storms did develop.

There were two authors and myself at this event, and even though I had some misgivings about the whole deal to start with, I tried to remain optimistic about the situation. The event was to last three hours—from three in the afternoon until six in the evening.

As it turned out, there weren't any customers that showed up. Towards the later afternoon, I caught myself thinking, *This store manager arranges these book signings so she has someone to talk to in the last few hours before she closes for the day!*

The book signing was a bust! You could say that it was an *uneventful* event.

Trouble Again

I got in trouble again at the ski area. It really wasn't my fault, although I was the instigator of it.

A lot of parents will use a harness-type apparatus to teach their kids how to ski. The deal looks like a harness on a horse-and-buggy rig. The parent follows the child, controlling the speed of the youngster and stopping the kid by pulling him down. Yes, the kid falls, but I guess that's better than running into a tree or a lift tower.

It's one way to teach skiing to the youngsters and, I guess, relatively safe. It is kinda neat to see a parent using this method with the really young kids.

I had a class of adult students at the top of a hill. They were all lined up, ready to receive their instructions for the next lesson, when I noticed a mother teaching her child how to ski using a harness apparatus.

Without thinking, I hollered out to the child, "Hey there young lady, next time make your mom pull *you* down the hill!"

This comment brought a big smile from the youngster and a good laugh from my students. However, the mother of the child didn't think it was too funny, and proceeded to inform me exactly why! My thoughts as she left were not too complementary, and I wondered why Mom didn't just put the youngster in ski school and go off and do her own skiing.

I have since said the same thing to many youngsters learning how to ski in the same fashion, but with considerably better results.

There are a lot of ways to ski; however, there are two ways to ski improperly. One is to ski out of control. The other is to ski and not have any fun!

Other Books by Stu Campbell

Horsing Around a Lot

Horsing Around the Dudes

Humor Around Horses